Questions in
Higher
Biology

Text © 2003 Andrew Morton
Design and layout © 2003 Leckie & Leckie Ltd
Cover image © Lawrence Lawry/Science Photo Library

08/100908

All rights reserved. No part of this publication may be stored in a retrieval system, or transmitted in any form or by any means, electronic, mechanical, photocopying, recording or otherwise, without prior permission in writing from Leckie & Leckie Ltd. Legal action will be taken by Leckie & Leckie Ltd against any infringement of our copyright.

The right of Andrew Morton to be identified as author of this work has been asserted by him in accordance with sections 77 and 78 of the Copyright, Designs and Patents Act 1988.

ISBN 978-1-898890-46-1

Published by
Leckie & Leckie Ltd, 3rd floor, 4 Queen Street, Edinburgh, EH2 1JE

Tel: 0131 220 6831 Fax: 0131 225 9987

enquiries@leckieandleckie.co.uk   www.leckieandleckie.co.uk

Edited by George Milne

Special thanks to
Julie Barclay (design), Latte Goldstein (cover design), Merlyn Gudgeon (illustration) and Alison Irving (proofreading)

A CIP Catalogue record for this book is available from the British Library.

Leckie & Leckie Ltd is a division of Huveaux plc.

Andrew Morton

Contents

Introduction

This book is designed to be used as a companion study guide to *Higher Biology Course Notes*, published by Leckie & Leckie.

Its aim is to allow you to revise effectively for the Scottish Qualifications Authority's Higher Biology examinations. As such, additional information is given relating to the unit tests and the course examination. The Higher Biology course is divided into 3 units. At the end of each unit you must pass a short forty-five minute test of 40 marks. The pass mark for each test is 26 (65%). If you fail a unit test you will be given another opportunity to pass a different unit test set to the same standard. You must also write up **one** practical investigation, which will be marked by your teacher or lecturer.

At the end of the course, you sit an extended course examination paper which tests your knowledge of all three units in an integrative way. The course examination will be more difficult and the pass mark will normally be fixed at around 50%. If you pass, you will be graded A, B, C or D according to your mark. To be sure of an 'A' pass, you should aim to achieve 75% or more in the course examination.

The course examination is 2 hours and 30 minutes long and will normally be offered in May of each year.

The examination has three sections comprising 130 marks in total.

Section A 30 multiple-choice questions   30 marks
Section B Short-answer questions   80 marks
Section C Two extended-answer questions   20 marks

The examination contains questions which test your biological knowledge and your ability to deal with data and solve problems. This book contains examples of these types of questions.

Section A
Thirty multiple-choice questions are given as examples on pages 33 to 35.

Section B
The questions on pages 4 to 32 are mostly of the type you will come across in section B of the examination.

Section C
The extended-answer questions require you to write two short essays with or without tables, bullet points and diagrams. There is a choice of one out of two topics for each of the questions.

In the second essay, you are given two marks for the **coherence** and **relevance** of your response. So you must write in a logical order, with proper paragraphs and sentences, and you must stick to the topic. Correct spelling is helpful but rarely essential. Only where words such as glucagon and glycogen might be confused is spelling imperative. Each essay should take up around one page of A4 paper.

The relevant pages for each of the three units in Leckie and Leckie's *Higher Biology Revision Notes* are given in the table below.

Unit	Title of Unit (40 classroom hours each)	Relevant pages in Leckie & Leckie's *Higher Biology Revision Notes*
1	Cell Biology	5 – 19
2	Genetics, Evolution and Adaptation	20 – 49
3	Control and Regulation	50 – 63

You will find that by reading the appropriate pages in Leckie & Leckie's *Higher Biology Revision Notes* you should be able to answer most of the questions. The green pages in this book provide answers. Try to resist the temptation to look at them until after you have made a serious attempt at each question.

Throughout the book, reference is made to the Higher Biology syllabus. This is part of the Arrangements document published by the SQA. The syllabus simply tells your teacher or lecturer what to teach you and gives an indication of the depth of study for each topic. A simplified summary of the syllabus is given at the start of each section to outline the knowledge required to pass the unit tests and the course examination. At the end of the book there are five pages listing all the key words and phrases which actually appear in the syllabus, or which have appeared in past examination papers. This list can be used as a useful check of your knowledge. These key words appear in **bold** in the companion text.

Some knowledge of Standard Grade or Intermediate 2 Biology will also be of value. You may obtain a copy of Leckie & Leckie's *Standard Grade Biology Revision Notes* and *Intermediate 2 Biology Success guide* from your school, college or bookshop. Questions which require some Intermediate 2 or Standard Grade knowledge are marked ‡.

Unit 1. Cell Biology

CELL STRUCTURE IN RELATION TO FUNCTION

- Be able to relate structure to function in cells of different tissue types and in unicellular organisms.
- Know the differences between diffusion, osmosis and active transport, and know about the role of the cell wall and plasma membrane in relation to these processes.
- Be able to describe the fluid-mosaic model of the cell membrane.
- Know that plant cells full of water are turgid, and those short of water become flaccid or even plasmolysed (membrane becomes separated from the inside of the cell wall).
- Know that a solution which is more dilute than another solution is hypotonic to the stronger (more concentrated) solution, and the stronger solution is hypertonic to the weaker (more dilute) solution.

---

1. (a) Identify any three different cell types in the cross-section of the leaf and give one function of each. ‡

    (b) What are the functions of the two compounds labelled in the diagrams below? ‡

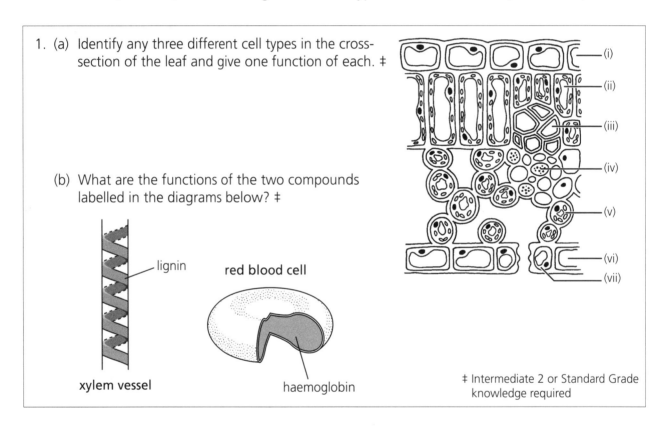

lignin

xylem vessel

red blood cell

haemoglobin

‡ Intermediate 2 or Standard Grade knowledge required

---

2. Construct a branched or paired statement key to enable the following unicellular organisms to be identified. ‡

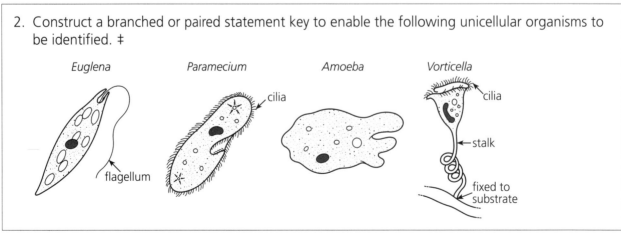

Euglena

Paramecium

cilia

Amoeba

Vorticella

cilia

stalk

flagellum

fixed to substrate

---

3. (a) Name the cell organelle which:
   (i) carries out photosynthesis
   (ii) is the site of protein synthesis
   (iii) packages substances before secretion
   (iv) is the site of RNA synthesis
   (v) controls the activity of the cell
   (vi) is the site of aerobic respiration
   (vii) transports material around the cell
   (viii) provides a store of water and mineral salts for plant cells. ‡

   (b) Suggest a function for each of the proteins P and Q in the diagram of the membrane shown below.

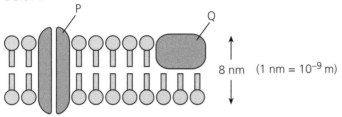

   8 nm $(1 \text{ nm} = 10^{-9} \text{ m})$

4. (a) What term is used to describe the diffusion of water through a membrane?

   (b) What name is given to the membrane which surrounds the cell, to distinguish it from other membranes in the cell?

   (c) The diagram below shows three plant cells which have been placed in salt solutions of different strengths.

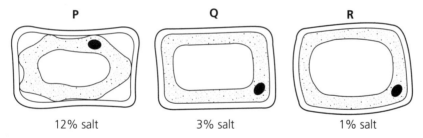

P	Q	R
12% salt	3% salt	1% salt

   (i) Which cell is plasmolysed?
   (ii) What other term could be used to describe the plasmolysed cell?
   (iii) Which cell is likely to be turgid?

   (d) The graph shows the effect of temperature on the uptake of ions by an algal cell.
   (i) What is the optimum temperature for ion uptake?
   (ii) Why does temperature affect the rate of uptake of ions by the cell?
   (iii) Account for the change in rate of ion uptake at high temperatures.
   (iv) What term is used to describe ion uptake that takes place against a concentration gradient?

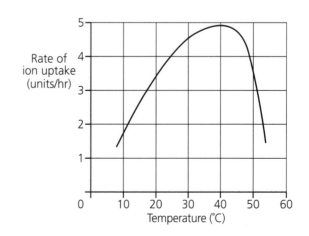

See pages 6, 8 and 9 of Leckie & Leckie's *Higher Biology Course Notes*.
© Leckie & Leckie

PHOTOSYNTHESIS

- Know the different fates of light landing on a leaf.
- Be able to distinguish between absorption and action spectra.
- Be able to describe the role of chlorophyll and other photosynthetic pigments.
- Be able to describe how photosynthetic pigments can be separated by chromatography.
- Know the detailed structure and function of a chloroplast.
- Be able to describe the processes of the light-dependent and light-independent reactions.
- Know about the chemicals ATP, ADP, RuBP, GP and NADP (the initials are sufficient) and their roles in photosynthesis.
- Be able to state the number of carbon atoms of compounds at each stage in the process.

---

5. (a) Why do leaves appear green in colour?

   (b) What name is given to a graph which shows:
      (i) which wavelengths (colours) of light are absorbed by a pigment?
      (ii) how well a plant photosynthesises in different wavelengths of light?

   (c) What is the advantage to a plant of having more than one photosynthetic pigment?

---

6. Use the words **grana** or **stroma** to answer the questions which follow:

   (a) Where does photolysis take place?

   (b) Where are the photosynthetic pigments found?

   (c) Where are enzymes involved in the Calvin cycle found?

   (d) Where is light energy absorbed in a chloroplast?

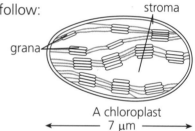
A chloroplast
← 7 μm →

---

7. Use the words **light** or **dark** after each statement to indicate whether the statement refers to the light-dependent (light) stage or light-independent (dark) stage of photosynthesis (sometimes called the Calvin cycle or carbon fixation).

   (a) Oxygen is a by-product.   (b) Glucose is the end product.

   (c) Carbon dioxide is fixed.   (d) ATP is converted to ADP + P_i.

---

8. (a) Name the **two** substances produced during the light-dependent stage which are required for the fixation of carbon during the Calvin cycle.

   (b) What are the energy sources of
      (i) the light reaction?
      (ii) the Calvin cycle (dark reaction)?

   (c) (i) Name the 5-carbon compound which acts as a carbon dioxide acceptor.
      (ii) Name the 3-carbon compound which is reduced during the Calvin cycle.
      (iii) What is the function of NADP in photosynthesis?

RESPIRATION

- Know the importance of ATP to living things.
- Be able to describe the three stages of aerobic respiration in some detail.
- Know about the chemicals: glucose, pyruvic acid, acetyl CoA, citric acid and NAD.
- Be able to describe the detailed structure and function of a mitochondrion.
- Be able to distinguish between anaerobic and aerobic respiration.
- Be able to state the number of carbon atoms of compounds at each stage.
- Know that fats and proteins are alternative respiratory substrates.
- Be aware of the role of enzymes as catalysts in metabolic pathways.
- Be able to distinguish between oxidation and reduction reactions as they relate to respiration.

9. The process of cellular respiration takes place in _____ living cells to provide energy in the form of _____. This energy-rich compound is manufactured from _____ and P_i. The first stage of respiration occurs in the _____ of the cell and is called _____. During this stage, glucose, a _____ carbon compound, is broken down to a 3-carbon compound called _____ acid. If _____ gas is available, the 3-carbon compound enters the _____ and is converted to _____. The acetic acid (2 carbon) part of this molecule then joins with a 4-carbon compound to form a 6-carbon compound called _____ acid. This second stage is called the _____ cycle and occurs in the _____ of the mitochondria. During this second stage, _____ atoms are removed from the 6-carbon compound in the form of _____ _____. At the same time _____ is removed and combines with a carrier called _____. The carrier compound passes the _____ to a series of carriers in the _____ _____ which are found on the _____ of the mitochondria. As each carrier is reduced and _____ in turn, ATP is produced. At the end of the chain the final acceptor of the hydrogen is _____. When these two substances combine _____ is formed as an end product. The total gain from the aerobic breakdown of one molecule of glucose is ____ molecules of ATP. If no oxygen is present then the stages _____ and _____ cannot take place. Instead, only ___ molecules of ATP are produced. This type of respiration is described as _____. In animals and plants, toxic compounds are also produced as a result of anaerobic respiration. In animals the compound is _____ _____ and in plants two compounds are produced, _____ _____ and _____. The anaerobic respiration of yeast is used commercially in two major processes, _____ and _____.
Compounds other than glucose can also be used as respiratory substrates, e.g. _____ and _____.

DNA, RNA AND PROTEIN SYNTHESIS

- Know the structure of the DNA molecule and how it replicates.

- Know the simple structure of proteins, i.e. fibrous and globular.

- Be able to describe the role of DNA, mRNA and tRNA in protein synthesis.

- Be able to describe the structure and function of rough and smooth endoplasmic reticulum (ER), the ribosomes and the Golgi apparatus (Golgi body) as they relate to protein synthesis.

10. (a) Give an example of a fibrous protein and a globular protein and give **one** function of each.

    (b) Name **four** chemical elements essential for the manufacture of protein. ‡

    (c) Name the sub-units from which proteins are made.

11. (a) The diagram below shows a DNA molecule undergoing replication.

    (i) Name the bases 1, 2 and 3.
    (ii) Name the components labelled 4 and 5.
    (iii) Name the unit labelled 6.
    (iv) Name the type of bond found at 7.

    (b) What name, given to the DNA molecule, describes its shape?

    (c) Name **three** compounds needed by cells to enable DNA replication to take place.

12. The answers to the following questions are all whole numbers.

    (a) How many bases code for one amino acid?

    (b) How many different types of base are found in a molecule of DNA?

    (c) How many different types of amino acid are used in the manufacture of protein?

13. What dictates the sequence of amino acids in a protein molecule?

CELLULAR RESPONSE IN DEFENCE

- Be able to describe the simple structure of a virus.
- Know how viruses replicate (make copies of themselves) in other cells.
- Be able to describe phagocytosis and the activity of lysosomes in the destruction of foreign cells.
- Know that some lymphocytes can produce antibodies in response to foreign antigens.
- Be able to describe problems of tissue rejection and use of suppressor drugs in tissue transplantation.
- Know that plants can produce a variety of toxic compounds, e.g. tannins, cyanide, nicotine and resin, to defend themselves.

---

14. (a) Name the **two** compounds of which viruses are principally composed.

    (b) Describe **two** features of viruses which enable them to be classified as 'living'.

    (c) How many microns (μm) are there in a metre?

---

15. (a) The diagram below shows the replication of a virus.
       For each of the stages (i) to (v), suggest a suitable description.

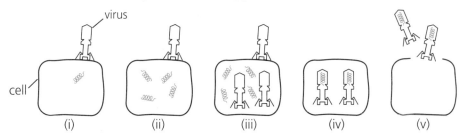

    (b) What happens to the cell after the virus has completed its reproductive cycle?

---

16. The diagram shows a cell engulfing a bacterium.

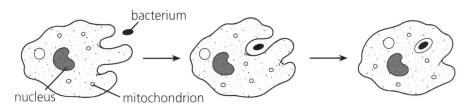

    (a) (i) What name is given to this process?
         (ii) Name the cell organelles which contain enzymes to digest the bacterium.
         (iii) Where are cells of this type found in the human body?

    (b) What name is used to describe the compounds on the surface of cells which can be recognised by the body as being 'self' or 'non-self'?

    (c) Name the proteins produced by lymphocytes in response to the presence of foreign substances or foreign cells.

    (d) Name a substance produced by some trees to protect damaged bark.

Unit 2. Genetics, Evolution and Adaptation

MEIOSIS

- Know that sexual reproduction is a means of enabling genetic variation to be maintained in a population and be able to explain the significance of this in the evolution of life on Earth.

- Be able to outline the process of meiosis in relation to the production of gametes which are haploid and genetically different. (The names of the stages need not be known.)

17. Complete the following table to show some differences between mitosis and meiosis. ‡

Feature	Mitosis	Meiosis
What is the genetic complement of the daughter cells? *haploid/diploid*		
What types of daughter cells are produced? *body cells/gametes*		
Are daughter cells genetically identical? *no/yes*		
Do homologous chromosomes pair up? *no/yes*		

18. The diagram shows a cell undergoing division.

    (a) (i) Is the nucleus dividing by mitosis or meiosis? ‡
    (ii) Give a reason for your answer.

    (b) How many chromosomes are shown in the diagram?

    (c) How many chromosomes will be present in one daughter cell?

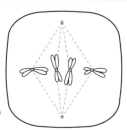

19. (a) Name **two** processes occurring during meiosis which result in the recombination of genes to produce genetically different gametes.

    (b) (i) At which stage in meiosis is the chromosome number of the cells halved?
    (ii) Why is it important that the chromosome number is halved?

    (c) The diagram shows two homologous chromosomes, one with the alleles **A** and **B** and the other with the alleles **a** and **b**. A chiasma is also shown.
    State the genotype of the four gametes formed as a result of crossing over at this chiasma.

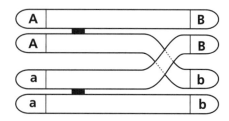

GENETICS

- Be able to solve monohybrid, sex-linked and dihybrid genetics problems to the F_2 generation.

- Understand the difference between genes which are linked and those which are not linked.

- Know how to map the position of 3 or 4 linked genes on chromosomes using recombination frequencies.

---

20. State the genetic terms for each of the following: ‡

    (a) a sex cell

    (b) a different form of a gene

    (c) an allele which only affects the phenotype when two copies of this allele are present

    (d) an allele which always affects the phenotype

    (e) having a pair of identical alleles

    (f) having two different alleles

    (g) the appearance of an organism with respect to its genes

    (h) the genetic make-up of an organism.

---

21. In humans the allele for fixed ear lobes (**e**) is recessive to the allele for free ear lobes (**E**) and the trait (characteristic) is not sex-linked.
    The diagram below shows the inheritance of ear lobes in a family.

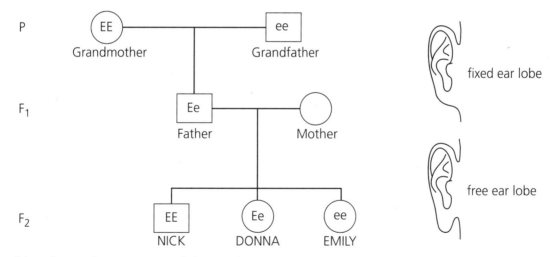

    (a) What is the genotype of the mother?

    (b) What is the phenotype of the father?

    (c) (i) What is the ratio of individuals with free ear lobes to fixed ear lobes in the F_2 generation?
        (ii) Is this the same ratio as the expected ratio?

    (d) Donna marries a man with fixed ear lobes and they have a daughter.
        (i) What is the chance that the daughter will have free ear lobes?
        (ii) What is the chance that a second daughter will have free ear lobes?

---

22. Haemophilia is a sex-linked condition in humans and the allele for haemophilia is recessive.

    (a) Can a father pass the recessive allele to his son?

    (b) Can a carrier woman pass the recessive allele to her daughter?

    (c) Can a man and woman who have normal blood have an affected child?

23. The genes P and Q are found on different chromosomes, i.e. they are not linked.
    How many gametes of different genotypes can be formed from the following individuals?

    (a) PPqq

    (b) PpQQ

    (c) PpQq

24. In pea plants, the gene for height has two alleles: **T** (tall) and **t** (dwarf), and the gene for flower colour has two alleles: **C** (coloured) and **c** (white). These two genes are found on separate chromosomes.

    Two heterozygous plants are crossed.

    (a) What proportion of the offspring would be expected to be heterozygous for both genes?

    (b) What proportion of the offspring would be expected to be tall?

    (c) What proportion of the offspring would be expected to be both dwarf and white?

25. (a) Construct a Punnett square to show the genotypes of the F_1 offspring produced when a pea plant with genotype **TTCc** is crossed with a pea plant with genotype **TtCC**.

    (b) Would the seedlings grown from this cross have the same phenotype?

26. In tomato plants the dominant allele A gives **purple** stems and the recessive allele **a** gives **green** stems. Allele B gives a **cut** leaf shape and the recessive allele **b** gives a **potato** leaf shape.

    (a) What is the genotype of a true breeding, green-stemmed cut-leaf plant?

    (b) What are the genotypes of the gametes of a plant heterozygous for both genes, assuming the genes are not linked?

    (c) If the genes are linked and crossing-over occurs during gamete formation, what differences, if any, would there be in the genotypes of the gametes compared with your answer to (b)?

    (d) A heterozygous plant is test-crossed (i.e. crossed with an individual of genotype **aabb**) and the following results are obtained:
        109 purple cut   103 purple potato   6 green cut   10 green potato.
        Are the genes linked? Give a reason for your answer.

MUTATION

- Know how mutations arise and be able to describe the different types of base, gene and chromosome mutation, e.g. substitution, insertion, deletion, duplication, translocation.
- Be able to describe how non-disjunction gives rise to polyploidy.
- Know that polyploidy is used in agriculture to improve crop plants.
- Know how base mutations can affect amino acid sequences.
- Know that mutations are the raw material for evolution.

---

27. (a) What effect do mutations have on the genotypes of organisms?

    (b) Give **two** examples of environmental factors (mutagens) which increase mutation rates.

    (c) Why are mutations important?

---

28. A segment of a chromosome is represented as

    A B C D E F G H I J K L M

    A number of mutant versions of this segment are shown below.
    Give the names of the different types of chromosome mutation which have occurred.

    (a) A B C D E F J I H G K L M

    (b) A B C D E G H I J K L M

    (c) A B C D E F E F G H I J K L M

    (d) A B C D H I J K L M   E F G goes to another chromosome.

---

29. (a) The black mustard plant, with a diploid chromosome number of 16, is closely related to the cabbage plant with a diploid chromosome number of 18. These plants can be crossed to produce a sterile hybrid.
     (i) What is the haploid number of the black mustard plant?
     (ii) If the haploid gamete of a black mustard plant fuses successfully with a haploid gamete from a cabbage plant, what would be the diploid number of an F_1 plant?
     (iii) Such F_1 plants are often sterile. Why is this so?

    (b) The zygote from such a cross undergoes complete non-disjunction. The resulting plant has double the normal diploid number of chromosomes and is fertile.
     (i) What term is used to describe plants with more than the diploid number of chromosomes?
     (ii) Why are such plants often fertile?
     (iii) What are the advantages of polyploidy in crop production?

    (c) (i) Describe briefly what happens to the chromosomes in a cell which undergoes complete non-disjunction during meiosis.
     (ii) What term describes a gamete which has an extra set of chromosomes?

NATURAL SELECTION

- Be able to define a species as a group of similar organisms able to produce fertile offspring.

- Know that organisms best suited to their environment survive to reproduce and that organisms unable to adapt to changing conditions become extinct.

- Know that isolation mechanisms are essential for the evolution of new species by natural selection.

- Be able to describe the adaptive radiation of organisms to new environments, leading to speciation, e.g. as shown by Galapagos finches.

- Know about the high-speed evolution of organisms such as bacteria and the peppered moth.

- Be able to describe different methods used by humans to conserve species in danger of extinction.

---

30. Outline the key features of Darwin's theory of evolution by natural selection.

---

31. (a) In a study of the distribution of peppered moths, 95% of the moths found near a city were black, whereas 99% of the moths found in a country area were speckled white.
    (i) What term is used to describe the black form of the peppered moth?
    (ii) Explain why the bark of trees in industrial areas is sometimes black.
    (iii) What 'pollution indicator' plant often grows on tree trunks in country areas, giving them a grey-white speckled appearance? ‡
    (iv) Explain why the black form of the peppered moth is more common in industrial areas.
    (v) Following the introduction of smokeless zones, the black form of the peppered moth is becoming less common in cities. Give an explanation for this change.

    (b) The dark form of the peppered moth is often given as an example of 'high-speed evolution'. Give another example of 'high-speed evolution'.

---

32. (a) State **two** naturally occurring processes which are important sources of variation in living organisms.

    (b) Why is variation within a species an aid to the survival of members of that species?

    (c) Give **two** examples of isolating mechanisms which can lead to speciation.

    (d) What term is used to describe the evolution of a number of different related species from a common ancestor, each adapted to a different environment?

    (e) What is meant by the term *'ecological niche'*?

    (f) The diagram shows the evolutionary relationship between three species of finch on the Galapagos islands. For any **one** finch, describe how its beak is adapted to feeding.

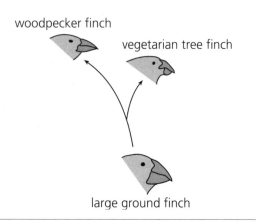

woodpecker finch

vegetarian tree finch

large ground finch

ARTIFICIAL SELECTION

- Know that domesticated animals and crop plants are the end-products of hundreds of years of artificial selection by humans.

- Know that hybridisation is the crossing of individuals with marked differences which can result in the production of offspring with combinations of desirable characteristics.

- Be able to describe some simple techniques in genetic engineering and somatic fusion of plants to produce new species/varieties of plants and animals.

- Know that genes can be located on chromosomes using gene probes or by the recognition of characteristic banding patterns on the chromosomes.

- Be able to describe the production of insulin by genetic engineering of bacterial plasmids.

- Know the function of the enzymes: endonuclease, ligase and cellulase in these processes.

---

33. (a) (i) Describe one way in which artificial selection is similar to natural selection.
    (ii) Describe one way in which artificial selection is different from natural selection.

    (b) Give an example of a feature of cattle improved by artificial selection.

    (c) What term is used to describe the breeding of individuals with useful characteristics from different genetic stock?

---

34. (a) Name the two types of enzyme used to splice genes into bacterial plasmids and describe the function of each.

    (b) Name a human hormone which can be produced by genetically engineered bacteria. ‡

    (c) Describe one way by which scientists can locate the position of genes on chromosomes.

---

35. The diagram below shows the removal of the cell wall from a plant cell as part of an artificial breeding technique.

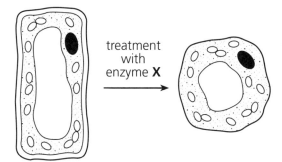

treatment with enzyme **X**

    (a) Name enzyme **X**.
    (b) What name is given to the plant cell after treatment?
    (c) Why has the cell wall been removed from the plant cell?
    (d) What term is used to describe this breeding technique?
    (e) Why is this technique particularly useful in plant breeding?

MAINTAINING A WATER BALANCE IN ANIMALS

- Be able to describe methods of osmoregulation in marine and freshwater fish, e.g. salmon.
- Be able to describe some physiological and behavioural adaptations of mammals, e.g. desert rat, to living in deserts.

36. Choose the correct alternative from each pair of words in **bold** to make the following sentences read correctly.

> Freshwater fish live in a **hypertonic/hypotonic** medium. As a consequence they **take in/expel** water through their gills by **osmosis/active transport**. To compensate for this, they secrete **large/small** volumes of urine. This results in the **loss/uptake** of salts which has to be balanced by the **loss/uptake** of salts by **diffusion/active transport** through the **gills/nephrons**.

37. The diagram opposite shows a kidney nephron ‡ from a gerbil. Gerbils are found in dry desert regions.

    (a) (i) Describe **one** feature shown in the diagram which is an adaptation to living in dry conditions.
         (ii) Which label points to the area where ADH acts?

    (b) The table below gives the volumes of water produced when different foodstuffs are oxidised.

foodstuff which is oxidised (1 g of each)	volume of water produced (cm³)
glucose	0·56
fat	1·02

    (i) What is meant by the term 'metabolic water'?
    (ii) Which respiratory substrate is more likely to be used by gerbils?

    (c) Give **one** other example of a physiological adaptation of gerbils to desert life.

    (d) Give **two** examples of behavioural techniques used by gerbils to minimise water loss in hot dry weather.

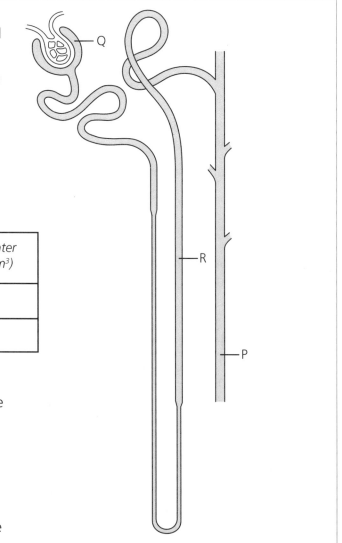

MAINTAINING A WATER BALANCE IN PLANTS

- Know the factors which help maintain the transpiration stream in plants, e.g. the opening and closing of stomata; the importance of the cohesive and adhesive forces which apply to the water molecules inside the plant; the significance of the root hairs.

- Know that the evaporation of water cools the leaves and results in mineral salts being drawn to the leaves in the transpiration stream.

- Know the effects of various environmental factors on the rate of transpiration, e.g. light, humidity, temperature, wind speed and atmospheric pressure.

- Be able to describe some adaptations of xerophytes (desert-living plants) and hydrophytes (freshwater-living plants).

---

38. The graph opposite shows the speed of water movement in the trunk and branches of a tree at various times on a summer day.

    (a) When does the water flow fastest through the:
        (i) trunk
        (ii) upper branches?

    (b) How do these figures support the theory that water is pulled up a tree rather than pushed up a tree?

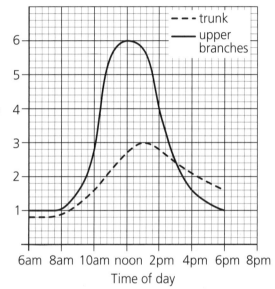

---

39. Part of a cross-section of a young root of a tree is shown below.

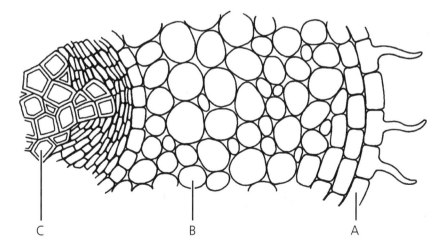

    (a) Name the **three** tissues shown, through which the water passes on its way to the trunk.

    (b) (i) Describe **one** feature of the root hairs which is an adaptation for water uptake.
        (ii) Describe **two** features of xylem vessels which are adaptations for water transport. ‡

---

40. In an investigation of transpiration in two species of plant (Geranium and Ivy) single leaves were removed from well-watered plants and treated in a variety of different ways. The table below summarises the treatments. Ten leaves were weighed before and after each treatment and the average weight loss was recorded in the table.

	Treatment of leaves	Conditions of exposure		Mean loss of mass of 10 leaves in each treatment (mg/mm^2 of leaf surface)	
		illumination	humidity	Geranium	Ivy
1	none	light	50%	5·7	11·2
2	none	dark	50%	0·8	0·4
3	none	light	100%	0	0
4	none	dark	100%	0	0
5	upper surface coated in Vaseline	light	50%	3·5	11·0
6	lower surface coated in Vaseline	light	50%	1·8	0·1

(a) Why were ten leaves used for each treatment?

(b) Why is water loss from the leaves lower in dark conditions?

(c) What **three** measurements must be made to be able to calculate the loss in mass/mm^2 of leaf surface for each of the plants?

(d) What do the results of the Vaseline treatments 5 and 6 disclose about the distribution of stomata on the leaves of both plants?

(e) (i) Why was no weight lost by the leaves in treatments 3 and 4?
    (ii) Why are these two treatments of value in this experiment?

(f) Which treatment enables a simple comparison to be made of the effectiveness of the waxy cuticles of the leaves of both species of plant?

(g) Describe the state of turgor of guard cells when stomata are fully open.

41. The diagram shows a cross-section through the curled leaf of marram grass. Marram is a xerophytic plant which is an early coloniser of sand dunes.

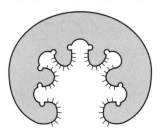

(a) Describe **three** leaf adaptations which help ensure a high humidity near the inner epidermis of the leaf.

(b) What effect does a high humidity have on the rate of evaporation?

OBTAINING FOOD – ANIMALS

- Understand what is meant by the economics of foraging behaviour in animals.
- Be able to describe interspecific and intraspecific competition in animals.
- Know the significance of dominance hierarchy and co-operative hunting in social animals.
- Be able to describe the importance of territorial behaviour in terms of intraspecific competition for food.

---

42. (a) Lions are carnivores which chase and kill their prey. There is a wide choice of animals to eat, but lions only choose to eat animals such as antelope, zebras and wildebeest. For each of the following, state why lions would not normally choose to hunt them:
     (i) leopard
     (ii) elephant
     (iii) mouse.

    (b) Describe **two** features of a lion's prey which would make it worthwhile for the lion to choose to hunt it.

    (c) Give the correct terms for each of the following forms of competition:
     (i) lions competing with lions for zebra
     (ii) lions competing with leopards for gazelle.

---

43. An investigation was carried out to find the optimum size of snail chosen by a species of bird for breaking open and eating. The table below shows the sizes of snails chosen by a number of birds over a period of time.

Mass of snails (g)									
0·6	0·7	0·9	1·2	1·1	1·2	0·4	0·4	1·5	1·6
1·2	2·0	1·2	0·9	1·0	1·9	1·5	0·4	1·8	1·4
1·0	1·7	0·9	1·1	0·3	0·8	1·4	0·9	1·6	1·6
1·1	2·1	1·7	1·0	0·4	1·2	1·3	0·3	1·7	0·8

(a) Group the data in the ranges [0–0·4], [0·5–0·9], [1·0–1·4], etc.
(b) Construct a histogram to display these results.
    (*A histogram is used to display continuous characteristics, whereas a bar chart is used to display discontinuous characteristics.*) ‡
(c) From the results, which range of mass of snails was the optimum choice of the birds?
(d) Suggest why it might not be economic for the birds to choose very small snails.
(e) Suggest why it might not be economic for the birds to choose large snails.

See pages 42, 43 and 44 of Leckie & Leckie's *Higher Biology Course Notes*.   © Leckie & Leckie

44. The graphs below show the relationship of size to aggression in cichlid male fish in competition for territory.

Graph A shows the relationship between the relative weights of two males and the length of the contest.

Graph B shows the probability of occurrence of four different forms of aggressive behaviour (circling, mouth wrestling, biting and tail beating) in relation to weight difference. The difference in size of the fish is expressed as a ratio, i.e. a weight ratio of 1·0 means that the fish are the same weight and a weight ratio of 2·0 means that one fish is twice as heavy as the other.

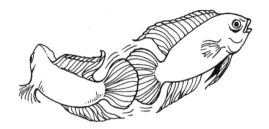

Two male cichlids tail beating

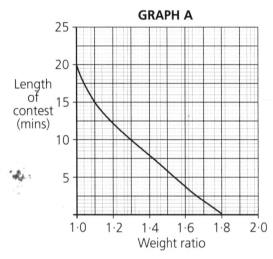

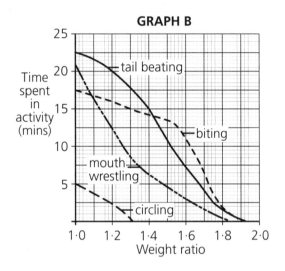

(a) From **Graph A**
   (i) What is the average length of a contest when both fish are the same weight?
   (ii) A male cichlid weighs 9 g. What is the minimum weight a lighter competitor would have to be before the two fish are likely to fight?

(b) From **Graph B**
   (i) What is the most common form of contest between fish of roughly the same weight?
   (ii) A male cichlid weighs 10 g and its aggessor weighs 8 g. For how long would they be expected to mouth wrestle?
   (iii) A male cichlid weighs 12 g and its aggressor weighs 8 g. What form of aggressive behaviour are the fish most likely to display when they meet?

(c) Suggest an advantage that circling and tail beating have over mouth wrestling.

(d) (i) Give **one** reason why many male animals compete with one another for territory.
   (ii) Give **one** example of a way by which a male mammal might mark the boundaries of its territory.

OBTAINING FOOD – PLANTS

- Be able to compare the sessility (immobility) of plants with the mobility of animals, i.e. plants make their own food using sunlight, carbon dioxide, water and minerals, so they do not have to move about. Animals have to eat other animals or plants, so they have to be able to move about to find their food.

- Know that plants compete with one another for light, water and soil nutrients/minerals.

- Understand the significance of the compensation point to shade and sun plants.

- Know that grazing by herbivores affects species diversity, e.g sheep and deer prevent the regeneration of forest in the Scottish Highlands.

---

45. The graph below shows rates of photosynthesis of two plant species in different light intensities.

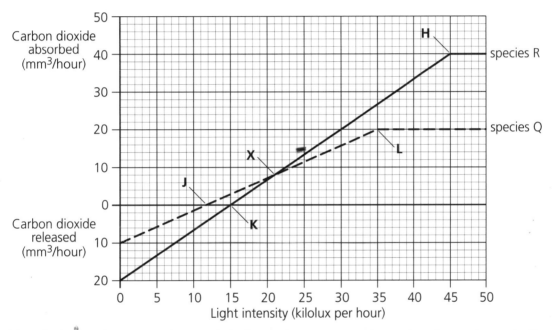

(a) Which **two** letters on the graph indicate the compensation points for each species?

(b) Which letter shows the light intensity at which the volume of CO_2 absorbed per hour in species Q is equal to the volume of CO_2 absorbed per hour in species R?

(c) (i) Which of the species is better adapted to growing in the shade?
    (ii) Give **two** features of the graph which support your answer.

(d) What is the factor which limits the rate of photosynthesis of species Q between points **J** and **L**?

(e) Suggest **one** factor which might limit the rate of photosynthesis of species R at light intensities of greater than 45 kilolux.

(f) (i) What measurements were taken to estimate the rates of photosynthesis in these species?
    (ii) Suggest another method by which the rate of photosynthesis might be measured.

(g) Apart from light, state **one** other abiotic factor for which plants compete.

COPING WITH DANGERS – ANIMALS

- Understand the significance of avoidance behaviour and habituation in animals.

- Know that the ability to learn from experience enables animals to avoid danger.

- Be able to describe some examples of individual and social mechanisms for defence.

46. An investigation was carried out to measure vigilance (sentry) behaviour in geese. Small isolated flocks of geese were observed over a period of weeks to see how much time was spent feeding and how much time was spent with heads raised checking for predators. The graph shows the results of the experiment.

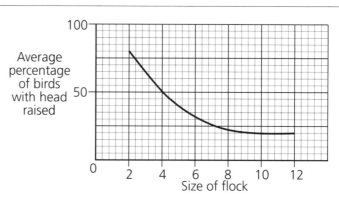

    (a) How many birds remained vigilant at any one time in flocks of
        (i) five birds?
        (ii) ten birds?

    (b) State the relationship between flock size and percentage vigilance.

    (c) Suggest why large flocks have a lower percentage of vigilance.

COPING WITH DANGERS – PLANTS

- Be able to describe some structural mechanisms for defence, e.g. stings, thorns, spines, bark, adopted by plants.

- Know the effects of grazing on the distribution of plant species and be able to describe some plant adaptations to survive grazing, e.g. low meristems (areas where cells divide actively), deep root systems and underground stems.

47. Certain species of plants such as daisies and plantain grow well on lawns. One feature they have in common is the possession of a flat rosette of leaves as shown in the illustration.

    (a) Give **two** advantages that the rosette of leaves gives to such plants when growing on a lawn.

    (b) What is a meristem?

    (c) Where is the meristem of grass leaves situated and why is this an advantage to grass plants?

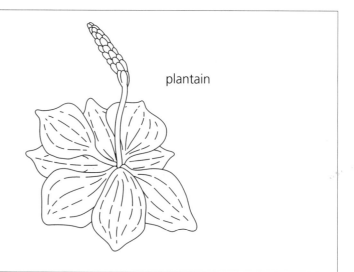

plantain

Unit 3. Control and Regulation

GROWTH IN PLANTS AND ANIMALS

- Be able to describe the growth patterns in plants and animals: in particular, in annual plants, trees, humans and locusts.

- Know that angiosperms have great powers of regeneration, whereas mammals have not. (Angiosperms are flowering plants, i.e. plants which produce seeds. Mammals are warm-blooded animals which suckle their young and possess hair.)

- Know that meristems are found in plants and not in animals.

- Know about the location and activity of meristems in flowering plants.

- Be able to identify annual rings in woody plants and describe how they are formed.

---

48. (a) The graph illustrates the growth pattern shown by locusts.

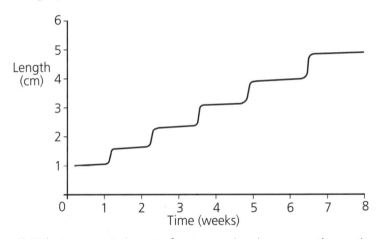

    (i) What prevents insects from growing in a smooth continuous way?
    (ii) How do insects overcome this problem of growth?

  (b) (i) Describe **two** ways in which the growth pattern of a tree differs from that of a human.
     (ii) In humans, growth accelerates between the ages of 10 and 14 years.
       What name is given to this stage in growth?

  (c) (i) Name a tissue type of mammals which can regenerate easily and a tissue type of mammals with very poor powers of regeneration.
     (ii) Compare the regeneration powers of a mouse and a geranium.

---

49. The diagram shows a longitudinal section from a growing stem of a flowering plant.
  (a) Name the meristems labelled P, Q and R.
  (b) State one activity which occurs in these areas and not in other areas of the stem.

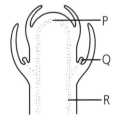

See pages 50, 51 and 52 of Leckie & Leckie's *Higher Biology Course Notes*. © Leckie & Leckie

50. (a) The diagram shows two cross-sections taken from different points on the same branch of a tree.

Section A

Section B

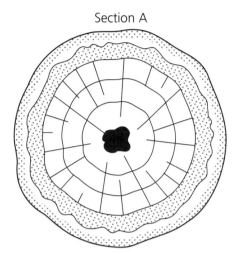
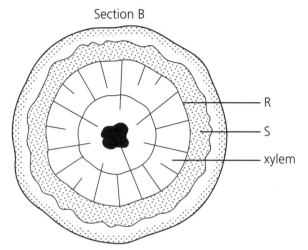

R

S

xylem

  (i) Name the tissues which would be found at R and S.
 (ii) State the age of each section of the branch.
(iii) Account for the different ages of each section from the same branch.
(iv) Describe the structural difference between spring wood and summer wood.
 (v) Describe **three** structural differences between a xylem vessel and a meristematic cell. ‡

(b) The diagram below shows a highly magnified view of a small area from one of the cross-sections drawn above.

R S T   U   V

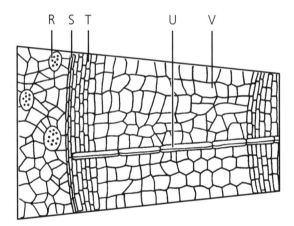

Which label points to:
 (i) spring wood
(ii) cambium tissue
(iii) phloem tissue?

(c) Estimate the season of the year when this section was cut and give a reason for your answer.

(d) Which of the cells shown below is most likely to be meristematic?

A nucleus 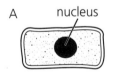   B vacuole 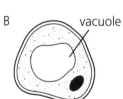   C  sieve plate   D 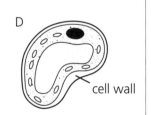 cell wall

GENETIC CONTROL OF GROWTH AND DEVELOPMENT

- Know that almost all cells in any organism contain a complete genetic code for the construction of that organism. This code is passed on from cell to cell by mitosis.
- Know that the genes of the genetic code control growth and development by being switched on and off in cells at appropriate times.
- Be able to describe the part played by genes in controlling metabolic pathways as shown in the case of phenylketonuria.
- Be able to describe the Jacob-Monod hypothesis as shown by the gene activity of the bacterium *E. coli* when it produces the enzyme galactosidase.
- Know the terms repressor molecule, regulator gene, inducer, operator and structural gene.

---

51. Sometimes an enzyme is absent from a cell due to a mutation. In such cases the metabolic pathway is blocked and very often the effect is lethal. For example, the absence of the enzyme which converts the amino acid phenylalanine to the amino acid tyrosine results in the condition in humans known as phenylketonuria (PKU).
The metabolic pathway is shown below:

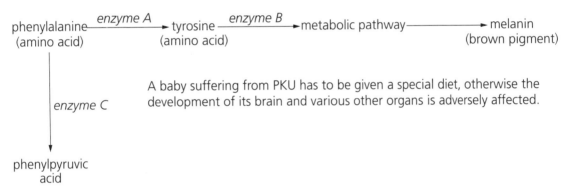

A baby suffering from PKU has to be given a special diet, otherwise the development of its brain and various other organs is adversely affected.

(a) The absence of which enzyme, shown in the pathway, brings about PKU?

(b) Name a substance which will accumulate if this enzyme is absent?

(c) Children suffering from PKU can still make some melanin. Suggest how they are able to make melanin despite the block in the metabolic pathway.

---

52. (a) In the Jacob-Monod hypothesis of gene action in the bacterium *E. coli*, what are the suggested functions of the following:
(i) the regulator gene
(ii) the operator
(iii) the structural gene?

(b) (i) What is the function of the repressor molecule?
(ii) Under what circumstances is the repressor molecule unable to act?

(c) (i) What is the name of the sugar which *E. coli* digests? (Note that the sugar molecule is referred to as the *inducer*.)
(ii) Explain why this mechanism for the manufacture of enzyme could be said to be efficient.

See pages 53 and 54 of Leckie & Leckie's *Higher Biology Course Notes*.   © Leckie & Leckie

THE CONTROL OF GROWTH BY THE ACTIVITY OF HORMONES

- Be able to describe the role of the pituitary gland in the control of growth and development in humans. It secretes human growth hormone (GH) and thyroid stimulating hormone (TSH). (Do not learn the different conditions which result from the over- or underactivity of various glands.)

- Be able to describe the effects of indole-acetic acid (IAA) in the control of growth and development in plants, e.g. sites of production, role in apical dominance, phototropism, leaf abscission and fruit formation. (Phototropism is a directional growth response of plants to light coming from one direction.)

- Be able to describe the effects of gibberellic acid (GA_3) in the control of growth and development in plants, e.g. on dormancy, growth of dwarf varieties and the production of α-amylase in barley grains.

- Know about the practical applications of plant growth substances, e.g. in the manufacture of herbicides (weedkillers) and rooting powders.

---

53. In humans, which hormone:

    (a) controls metabolic rate?

    (b) directly influences the activity of the thyroid gland?

    (c) promotes the growth of the skeleton and muscles?

    > Take your answers from the list below:
    > **TSH**
    > **thyroxine**
    > **growth hormone**
    >
    > Each answer may be used more than once or not at all.

---

54. (a) Complete the table below to show whether auxins (A), gibberellins (G) or both (B) play a part in each of the processes.

Process influenced by plant growth substances	Letters A, G or B
(i) promotion of α-amylase production in cereals	
(ii) promotion of phototropic responses	
(iii) stimulation of roots to grow on stem cuttings	
(iv) increase in length of shoots of dwarf pea plants	
(v) prevention of leaf abscission (leaf drop)	
(vi) apical dominance over side shoots	
(vii) elongation of plant cells	

(b) Where is IAA produced in plants and what effect does it have on developing cells?

(c) What is meant by the term '*apical dominance*'?

(d) Why do house-plant growers sometimes remove the leading shoots from pot plants?

---

55. An investigation was carried out on the germination of barley grains. A number of grains were soaked in water for an hour then cut in half and placed, cut-side down, on starch agar in two petri dishes. The grains were left for 24 hours, then the agar plate was flooded with dilute iodine solution. The effect of the iodine solution on the starch-agar is shown in the diagrams below.

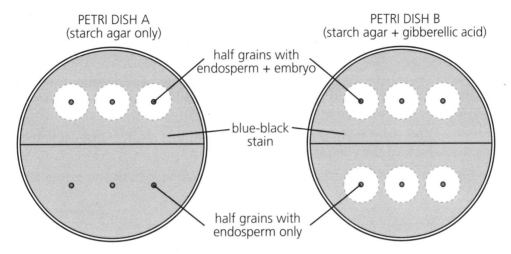

(a) What is the function of the iodine solution in this investigation?
(b) What may be deduced from the results in dish A?
(c) What may be deduced from the results in dish B compared with dish A?
(d) By comparing the results in dish A with those in dish B, suggest a hypothesis to explain how the embryo induces the digestion of starch.

56. (a) The diagram shows a barley grain cut in longitudinal section.
Which label indicates:
 (i) the aleurone layer
 (ii) the embryo
 (iii) the endosperm?

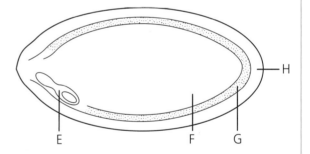

(b) In what part of the grain is gibberellic acid produced?

(c) (i) In what part of the grain is the enzyme α-amylase produced?
 (ii) What is the substrate for α-amylase?

(d) Why might it be necessary to convert glucose to starch for storage of energy?

57. Describe **two** practical uses of plant hormones in horticulture or agriculture.

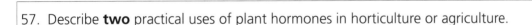

ENVIRONMENTAL CONTROL OF GROWTH

- Be able to describe the symptoms of deficiency of the macro-elements nitrogen, phosphorous, potassium and magnesium on the growth of plants.

- Know about the importance of iron, calcium and vitamin D to animals/humans.

- Know that heavy metals such as lead can affect the activity of enzymes.

- Be able to describe, in simple terms, the effects of thalidomide, alcohol and nicotine on human fetal development.

- Be able to describe the effects of light on the growth of plants in terms of directional light and day length, i.e. etiolation, phototropism and photoperiodism. (There is no need to know about the details of the phytochromes or the role of florigen.)

- Know that in phototropism, plant stems grow towards the light as a result of IAA causing cells to elongate on the shaded side of the plant stem.

- Understand the significance of day length to the timing of breeding in birds and mammals.

58. (a) (i) How do plants obtain the mineral salts they need for growth?
    (ii) How do animals obtain the mineral salts they need for growth?

   (b) Plants deprived of certain elements show deficiency symptoms.
        Describe **one** deficiency symptom for each of the following elements:
        (i) nitrogen
        (ii) phosphorous
        (iii) potassium
        (iv) magnesium.

   (c) For each of the following elements, name a compound found in plants in which that element would be present:
        (i) magnesium
        (ii) phosphorous
        (iii) nitrogen.

   (d) Which of the following drugs, *thalidomide*, *alcohol* or *nicotine*, has a record of causing limb deformity during fetal development?

   (e) The graph opposite shows the effect of different concentrations of lead on the activity of an enzyme.
        (i) At which concentration does lead start to have an effect on the activity of the enzyme?
        (ii) At which concentration does lead cease to be the limiting factor on the activity of the enzyme?

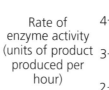

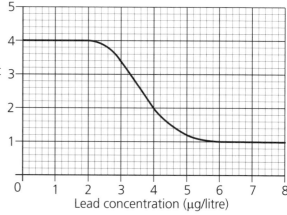

Rate of enzyme activity (units of product produced per hour)

Lead concentration (μg/litre)

59. The tables below record data on flowering in a species of plant.
The average number of flowers produced per plant is recorded at different temperatures and different night lengths.

Temperature = 15°C	
night length (hours)	number of flowers
5	9
6	10
7	10
8	3
9	0
10	0

Temperature = 20°C	
night length (hours)	number of flowers
5	18
6	17
7	15
8	15
9	16
10	0

(a) Is this species of plant a short-day or long-day plant?

(b) Describe **two** effects of temperature on flowering in this plant.

(c) (i) What term is used to describe an organism's response to a change in day or night length?
(ii) Describe a change in behaviour brought about in animals by a change in day length.

(d) In what area of the planet Earth does day length change least from season to season?

60. An experiment was set up to demonstrate the response of upright plant shoots (i) to light coming from one direction and (ii) to the hormone IAA. The diagrams below show the results of this experiment.

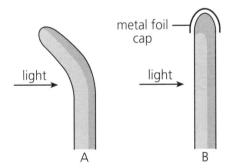
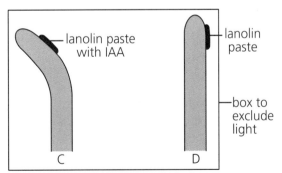

(a) What term is used to describe the response of shoot A to light?

(b) What does the growth of shoot C suggest about the response of the plant shoot to light?

(c) Why were shoots B and D included in the experiment?

PHYSIOLOGICAL HOMEOSTASIS

- Know about the importance of homeostasis (maintaining the steady state) in humans in terms of water content and glucose concentrations in the blood, and temperature control.
- Be able to describe negative feedback control as it applies to the action of the hormones anti-diuretic hormone (ADH), insulin, glucagon and adrenaline.
- Be able to define the terms endotherm (warm-blooded) and ectotherm (cold-blooded).
- Be able to describe the role of the hypothalamus and the skin in temperature control in humans.

---

61. (a) State whether each of the following sentences relating to anti-diuretic hormone (ADH) is **true** or **false**. If the statement is **false**, correct it by altering the word which is underlined.
    (i) ADH is produced by the <u>thyroid</u> gland.
    (ii) ADH is produced when we are <u>thirsty</u>.
    (iii) ADH causes kidney tubules to reabsorb <u>more</u> water.
    (iv) ADH has the effect of <u>decreasing</u> the volume of urine produced.

    (b) State whether each of the following sentences relating to maintaining glucose concentrations in the blood is **true** or **false**. If the statement is **false**, correct it by altering the word which is underlined.
    (i) The hormone insulin has the effect of <u>lowering</u> glucose concentrations in the blood.
    (ii) The hormones <u>adrenaline</u> and glucagon have similar effects on glucose concentrations in the blood.
    (iii) Glucagon and insulin are hormones produced by the <u>liver</u>.
    (iv) Glucose is stored as <u>starch</u> in the liver and muscles.

---

62. The diagram opposite shows a section through human skin.

    (a) Are humans endothermic or ectothermic animals?

    (b) Describe the action or activity of the following structures in cold weather:
    (i) the hair erector muscle
    (ii) the sweat gland.

    (c) Describe **one** feature shown in the diagram, other than the hair, which reduces heat loss.

    (d) (i) Describe the change in diameter of the capillary loop in warm weather.
    (ii) What term is used to describe this change to the capillaries?

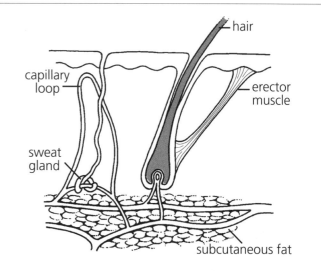

---

63. Describe negative feedback control as it relates to glucose concentrations in the blood and to the production of insulin.

POPULATION DYNAMICS

- Know that populations, although capable of increasing rapidly, often stay relatively constant in the long term.
- Be able to describe the influence of density-dependent and density-independent factors on the size of populations.
- Know that it is important to monitor populations for a wide variety of reasons: e.g. to control pests; to prevent extinction; as sources of food and raw materials; to monitor pollution using indicator species.
- Understand what is meant by the succession of plant species to climax communities.

---

64. (a) The *carrying capacity* of a habitat is defined as the maximum population of a given species that can be sustained in that habitat over a long period of time.

     The graph below shows changes in the numbers of red deer on an island during the 80 years which followed their introduction to the island in 1900.

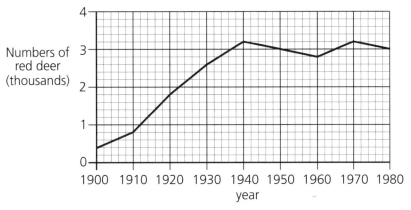

   (i) How many deer were introduced to the island in 1900?
   (ii) From the graph estimate the carrying capacity of this island for red deer.
   (iii) Suggest **two** density-dependent factors and **two** density-independent factors which might affect the carrying capacity of this island for red deer.
   (iv) Suggest **two** reasons why the population varied from 1940 onwards.
   (v) Give **three** reasons why it might be considered important to monitor the population of red deer on the island.

   (b) The graph opposite shows the size of a population of animals over a number of years.
      (i) For each point, P, Q and R, compare the birth rate with the death rate. ‡
         (Assume no emigration or immigration.)
      (ii) Why is the population increase small in the first year?

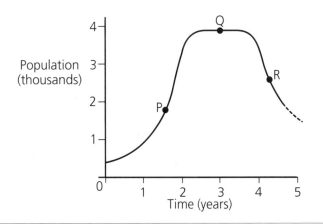

65. The diagrams below show a pond and the sequence of changes which have occurred to the habitat over a period of 50 years.

water

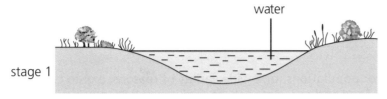

stage 1

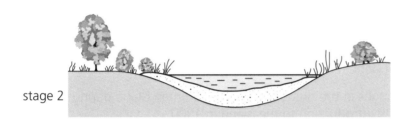

stage 2

Time

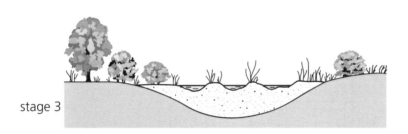

stage 3

stage 4

(a) (i) What name is given to this sequence of changes?
   (ii) What name is given to the final stable stage in this process?

(b) Name a plant which is an early coloniser of bare rock.

(c) Compare stages 1 and 4 in terms of biomass and complexity of food webs.

(d) How does the compensation point of plants living at ground level in a woodland compare with plants such as trees and bushes?

(e) What is meant by the term *habitat*? ‡

66. Describe **two** features of sand dunes which make them difficult places for plants to colonise.

Multiple Choice Questions

1. Which of the following processes does **not** require energy supplied in the form of ATP?

   A glycolysis
   B active transport
   C phagocytosis
   D osmosis

2. The fluid mosaic model is used to describe the nature of

   A cell membranes
   B transpiration
   C osmosis
   D kidney function.

3. Of what material are cell walls principally composed?

   A starch
   B lignin
   C cellulose
   D glycogen

4. In relation to the passage of materials, plant cell walls are described as

   A impermeable
   B permeable
   C waterproof
   D semi-permeable.

5. Which of the following lists the substances produced as a result of the light reaction of photosynthesis?

   A ATP and CO_2
   B ADP, oxygen and NAD(H)
   C ATP, oxygen and NADP(H)
   D ATP, water and NADP(H)

6. The table shows the end products of respiration in yeast, in addition to ATP. Which line is correct? ‡

	aerobic respiration	anaerobic respiration
A	oxygen and water	CO_2 and lactic acid
B	CO_2 and water	CO_2 and ethanol
C	CO_2 and water	oxygen and water
D	oxygen and water	CO_2 and ethanol

7. What is the anti-codon for the mRNA codon AUG?

   A UAC
   B TUC
   C TAC
   D ATG

8. The base code on a strand of DNA is ACT-GCA. What are the corresponding anti-codons on two tRNA molecules?

   A ACU and GCA
   B TGA and CGT
   C UGA and CGU
   D TGU and CGT

9. The formation of proteins from the DNA code is called

   A replication
   B transcription
   C translocation
   D translation.

10. Which of the following statements relating to meiosis is correct?

   A Chromatids separate during the first division.
   B Homologous chromosomes pair during the first division.
   C The chromosome number is halved at the second division.
   D Chiasmata appear after the first division is complete.

11. Two plants with the genotype **Hh** are crossed, and twenty-four seedlings are produced. How many seedlings would be expected to have the same genotype as the parent plants? ‡

    A   6
    B   8
    C   12
    D   18

12. A green-seeded pea plant is crossed with a yellow-seeded pea plant and half the offspring have green seeds. Which of the following statements relating to this cross is true? ‡

    A   The gene for green colouration is dominant.
    B   The offspring are all heterozygous.
    C   Half the offspring are homozygous.
    D   The expected ratio of green to yellow offspring is 3:1.

13. Colour-blindness is a sex-linked inherited condition. A family tree showing the inheritance of this condition is shown below. If the allele for normal vision is **N** and the allele for colour-blindness is **n**, what are the genotypes of the children P and Q?

    ▪ colour-blind male
    ☐ normal male
    ● colour-blind female
    ○ normal female

    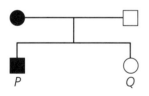

	P	Q
A	$X^n X^n$	$X^N Y$
B	$X Y^n$	$X^N X^N$
C	$X^n Y$	$X^N X^N$
D	$X^n Y$	$X^N X^n$

14. Linked genes are genes which

    A   have a similar effect
    B   affect both parents in a cross
    C   are found on the X chromosome
    D   are found on the same chromosome.

15. Four linked genes, W, X, Y and Z, recombine with the following frequencies: W and X: 7%; X and Y: 1%; Y and Z: 3%, W and Z: 3%. Which of the following shows the gene loci correctly?

16. A mutation, in which the base pair A-T is replaced by G-C, occurs in a strand of DNA. What term is used to describe this type of mutation?

    A   substitution
    B   translation
    C   inversion
    D   translocation

17. The organism *Escherichia coli*, often used in genetic engineering, is classified as

    A   a fungus
    B   a yeast
    C   an alga
    D   a bacterium.

18. A diagram to show the size, shape and number of chromosomes of an organism is called a

    A   genome
    B   genotype
    C   karyotype
    D   gene pool.

19. When total non-disjunction occurs during cell division it results in

    A   a clone
    B   polyploidy
    C   external fertilisation
    D   mitosis.

20. What part of the human brain monitors the temperature of the blood?

    A   hypothalamus
    B   medulla oblongata
    C   cerebellum
    D   cerebrum

21. Chloride secretory cells are found in the

    A   kidneys of desert mammals
    B   gills of marine bony fish
    C   root cortex of flowering plants
    D   stomata of hydrophytes.

22. Which of the following changes to the environment will often reduce evaporation of water from a leaf?

    A   decrease in humidity
    B   increase in wind speed
    C   decrease in light
    D   decrease in air pressure

23. Which of the following features would be least likely to be that of a hydrophyte?

    A   stomata on top surface of leaves
    B   reduced xylem tissue
    C   waxy cuticle on leaves
    D   air spaces in stem

24. An organism which is *sessile* is one which is

    A   fixed to one position
    B   photosynthesising
    C   avoiding danger
    D   reproducing.

25. Habituation is a form of behaviour in which the animal

    A   learns to carry out a simple behaviour by copying another animal
    B   learns not to respond to a repeated harmless stimulus
    C   always carries out the same response
    D   learns complex behaviour by repetition.

26. Which two hormones are secreted by the pituitary gland?

    A   thyroxine and GH
    B   adrenaline and TSH
    C   TSH and GH
    D   TSH and thyroxine

27. Which of the following chemical elements is present in all amino acids found in living organisms?

    A   potassium
    B   nitrogen
    C   phosphorous
    D   magnesium

28. Which of the following elements is a central component of the haemoglobin molecule?

    A   iron
    B   potassium
    C   magnesium
    D   calcium

29. Which of the following vitamins is required for the absorption of calcium from the intestine into the blood?

    A   vitamin A
    B   vitamin B
    C   vitamin C
    D   vitamin D

30. Which of the following best describes the process of etiolation?

    A   the development of lateral roots under the influence of IAA
    B   the growth of plant shoots towards or away from light
    C   the spindly growth of plants growing in low light conditions
    D   the stimulation of flowering in long-day and short-day plants

Higher Biology Vocabulary List

- The words and phrases which follow are specifically mentioned in the Higher Biology syllabus or have appeared in past examination papers.

- The definitions which accompany the words relate to the context in which they appear and are **not always blanket definitions**, e.g. α-amylase, alcohol, pancreas, phospholipid, transmission.

α-amylase .... an enzyme, produced in the aleurone layer, which digests starch in seeds

absorption spectrum .... a graph to show what wavelengths of light are absorbed by a pigment

accessory pigments .... coloured substances which absorb light and pass on the energy to chlorophyll

acetyl (2c) CoA .... a compound linking glycolysis with the Krebs cycle

action spectrum .... a graph to show the effects of different wavelengths of light on photosynthesis

active transport .... a method of transporting materials through membranes using ATP

adaptive radiation .... evolution of many species from one, to exploit new ecological niches

adhesion/cohesion .... the attraction of water molecules for one another and to other molecules

adrenaline .... a hormone produced by the adrenal glands for 'fight or flight' reaction

aerobic/anaerobic respiration .. respiration with and without oxygen respectively

alcohol .... a poison which influences fetal growth adversely

aleurone layer .... a layer of cells in seeds which produces α-amylase under the influence of GA_3

allele .... the alternatives of a gene, e.g. the alleles T (tall) and t (dwarf) of the gene for height

angiosperm .... a flowering plant

annual plant .... a plant which lives for one year or less

annual rings .... xylem pattern in wood which can be counted to give the age of a tree

antibody .... a protein produced by the body which inactivates foreign antigens

antibiotic .... a chemical which kills bacteria – it has no effect on viruses

antibiotic resistance .... the evolution of some bacteria to be able to survive antibiotics

anticodon .... triplet code of three bases found on tRNA which codes for one amino acid

anti-diuretic hormone .... ADH – a hormone produced by the pituitary in response to a lack of water

antigen .... a complex compound, usually a protein, which stimulates an antibody response

apical dominance .... the ability of growing shoots to prevent lateral buds from developing

apical meristem .... a meristem found at the growing tip of a plant shoot or root

artificial selection .... the selection of plants and animals by humans for breeding purposes

asexual reproduction .... reproduction without sex – produces identical offspring/a clone

ATP .... an energy-rich chemical which is needed to drive metabolism in all living cells

avoidance behaviour .... the ability of animals to escape danger by specific behaviour

biomass .... the total mass of organisms in an ecosystem or at one level in a pyramid of numbers

calcium .... a mineral requirement for bones, teeth, shells and for transmission of nerve impulses

Calvin cycle .... 2nd stage of photosynthesis – sometimes called 'dark' reaction or carbon fixation

captive breeding .... method of saving species by breeding, for example, in zoos

carbon fixation .... 2nd stage of photosynthesis, involving trapping carbon dioxide gas

carrier .... in genetics, a heterozygous organism carrying a potentially harmful recessive allele

cell bank .... a method of saving species by preserving gametes, somatic cells or seeds

cell sap .... a liquid found in plant cell vacuoles, gives turgor, and sometimes colour, to cells

cell wall .... permeable plant cell coating made principally of cellulose

cellulase .... an enzyme which digests cellulose, used in somatic cell fusion techniques

cellulose .... complex carbohydrate composed of glucose molecules – often called fibre

chiasmata .... points of attachment between homologous chromatids at the first stage of meiosis

chloride secretory cells .... specialised cells in fish gills which secrete salt

chlorotic .... a description of leaves which are pale yellow in colour

chromatid .... a daughter chromosome formed after DNA replication

chromatography .... a technique (often using absorbent paper) used to separate compounds

chromosome .... a densely coiled strand of DNA found in the nuclei of cells

© Leckie & Leckie

chromosome banding
    patterns .... patterns on chromosomes which are used to map gene loci (see locus)
citric acid .... a 6-carbon compound formed during the Krebs cycle
climax community .... the final stable community of organisms at the end of a succession
clone .... a group of genetically identical individuals produced asexually from one parent
collagen .... a tough fibrous protein found in bones, ligaments and tendons
codon .... the triplet code of three bases found on mRNA, which codes for one amino acid
compensation point.............. light intensity at which rates of photosynthesis and respiration are the same
conservation of species .... attempts by humans to prevent species from becoming extinct
co-operative hunting .... animal behaviour to maximise chances of catching prey
cortex of root .... plant tissue found between root hairs and central vascular bundle of roots
cristae .... inner folds of mitochondria on which cytochrome enzymes are found
crossing over .... the exchange/recombination of genes at chiasmata during meiosis
cyanide.................................. toxic compound made by some plants, e.g. clover, to discourage herbivores
cytochrome system .... third stage of aerobic respiration where ATP (and water) are produced
deficiency disease .... a growth or function disorder due to the lack of a mineral or vitamin
deletion .... a form of mutation where a base or gene is lost
density-dependent factor ...... a factor affecting a population, which is influenced by the size of the population
density-independent factor ... a factor affecting a population, which is not influenced by the size of the population
differentiation .... the specialisation of cells to carry out different functions
dihybrid cross .... a cross involving two pairs of alleles at different loci, e.g. AaBb × AaBb
diploid .... having two sets of chromosomes – one from each parent
dominance hierarchy .... behaviour in social animals where a pecking order is established
dormancy .... the ability of seeds to remain inactive for a period of time
Down's Syndrome................. a human condition which results from non-disjunction at meiosis
double helix.......................... the name given to the DNA molecule because of its shape
duplication .... a form of mutation in which a piece of chromosome is duplicated
ectotherm (cold-blooded) ..... an animal, e.g. a fish or reptile, which derives its heat from its surroundings
effector .... an organ which causes something to happen, e.g. a muscle or gland
electron transport system ..... another name for the cytochrome chain/system
endocrine gland .... a gland, e.g. pituitary gland, which produces hormones
endonuclease .... an enzyme used in genetic engineering to cut DNA
endoplasmic reticulum (ER) ... layers of membranes, sometimes with ribosomes, found in cells
endotherm (warm-blooded)... an animal, e.g. a mammal or bird, which derives its heat from its body metabolism
Eschericia coli .... gut bacterium often used in genetic engineering
epidemic .... widespread occurrence of a disease over a relatively short period of time
etiolated............................... the yellow spindly appearance of a plant grown in the dark or in poor light
extinction .... the permanent disappearance of a species due to death of all of its members
fibrous protein .... a protein with long tough molecules, e.g. collagen or fibrin
flaccid .... limp – description of a plant cell short of water
fluid mosaic model .... the model of a cell membrane describing its mobility and position of proteins
foraging behaviour .... animal behaviour in the search for food
gene pool .... all the genes in a population
gene probe........................... a method of identifying the locus of a gene, used in genetic engineering
gene switching .... the switching on and off of genes during development
genetic diversity................... the variety of genes in a species or population
genetic engineering .... the artificial transfer of genes from one organism to another
genome................................ the total DNA content of a cell or organism
genotype .... the genes an organism possesses; normally written as upper/lower case letters, e.g. Tt
gibberellic acid (GA$_3$) .... a plant growth substance
growth hormone (GH) .... a hormone which stimulates growth in mammals
globular protein.................... a spherically shaped protein, e.g. an enzyme or haemoglobin
glomerulus .... the coil of blood vessels found in the Bowman's capsule of a kidney nephron

Higher Biology Vocabulary List

glucagon .... a hormone which stimulates the conversion of glycogen to glucose

glycogen .... a storage carbohydrate found in animals – the equivalent of starch in plants

glycolysis .... the first stage of respiration, common to both anaerobic and aerobic respiration

Golgi apparatus .... a cell organelle involved in packaging materials prior to secretion

glycerate phosphate (GP) ...... a 3-carbon compound involved in the Calvin cycle of photosynthesis

habitat .... the place where an organism lives ‡

habituation .... animal behaviour in which an animal ceases to respond to a harmless stimulus

haemoglobin .... a red blood protein which carries oxygen

haploid .... half the normal diploid chromosome number. The chromosome number of gametes.

herbicide .... a weed killer, often containing plant hormones

heterozygous .... having two different alleles, e.g. Tt

high-speed evolution .... evolution of organisms which is fast enough to be monitored by humans

homeostasis .... keeping the steady state. For example, the liver is a homeostatic organ.

homologous chromosomes ... chromosomes, with identical gene loci, which pair up at meiosis

homozygous .... having pairs of identical alleles, e.g. tt or TT or AAbb

host .... an organism which is carrying a parasite, e.g. a bacterium can be the host of a virus

hybrid .... an organism produced as a result of hybridisation

hybridisation .... a cross where the parents are distinctly different from one another

hydrogen acceptor .... a compound which combines with hydrogen and is reduced in the process

hydrogen carrier .... a compound which carries hydrogen, e.g. NAD or NADP

hydrophyte .... a plant adapted to living in fresh water

hypertonic .... a solution which is stronger (more concentrated) than another solution

hypothalamus .... a monitoring centre in the brain which checks, e.g., the temperature of the blood

hypotonic .... a solution which is weaker (more dilute) than another solution

independent assortment of
     chromosomes .... the random positioning of chromosome pairs during the first division of meiosis

indicator species .... a species which indicates pollution levels, e.g. lichen, trout, sludge worms

indole-acetic acid (IAA) .... a plant growth substance or hormone

inducer .... e.g. lactose in the J-M hypothesis – causes *E. coli* to produce an enzyme to digest lactose

industrial melanism .... blackening of insects, e.g. peppered moth, due to a mutation

insecticide .... a chemical used to kill insects

interspecific competition ...... competition between individuals of different species

intraspecific competition ...... competition between individuals of the same species

insertion .... a form of mutation in which one or more bases are inserted in a strand of DNA

insulin .... a hormone which stimulates the removal of glucose from the blood

inversion .... a form of mutation in which bases are switched round

iron .... a mineral required for the manufacture of haemoglobin and hydrogen carriers

isolating mechanism .... in evolution, a factor which prevents two populations from breeding

Jacob-Monod (J-M) hypothesis .. a hypothesis which describes the switching on and off of genes

kidney tubule .... part of a nephron of a kidney where reabsorption takes place

karyotype .... a diagram showing the shape, size and numbers of chromosomes of a cell

Krebs cycle .... 2nd stage in aerobic respiration, occurs in matrix of mitochondria

lactic acid .... end product of (i) anaerobic respiration in muscles and (ii) souring of milk by bacteria

lactose .... milk sugar – see J-M hypothesis

lanolin .... an inert paste extracted from sheep's wool; often used to fix plant growth
                                             substances to plant parts

lead .... toxic heavy metal which can damage the nervous system of humans

leaf abscission .... leaf drop in autumn brought about by a reduction in IAA concentrations

ligase .... an enzyme used in genetic engineering to stick pieces of DNA together

'light' reaction .... the light-dependent stage of photosynthesis

linked genes .... genes found on the same chromosome, but at different loci (singular - locus)

liver .... a homeostatic organ with many functions, e.g storage of glycogen

locus .... the point on a chromosome where a gene is found

long-day/short-day plants ..... plants which flower in response to changes in day-length

© Leckie & Leckie

loop of Henle .... part of kidney nephron from where salts are pumped to improve water reabsorption

lymphocyte .... white blood cell which defends the body from foreign antigens

lysosome .... cell organelle which contains powerful digestive enzymes

macro-elements .... chemical elements, such as potassium and magnesium, which affect growth

magnesium .... a chemical element needed by plants to make chlorophyll

mammal .... a warm-blooded animal which suckles its young and does not lay eggs

meiosis .... a form of nuclear division to make haploid gametes

melanic .... a term used to describe the black mutant variety of insects, e.g. peppered moth

meristem .... an area in plants containing actively dividing cells

mesophyll .... photosynthetic cells (spongy and palisade) found in leaves ‡

metabolism .... the sum total of all the chemical reactions taking place in an organism

monitoring populations .... checking the size of populations of animals and plants

mutagen .... something which causes mutations to take place, e.g. atomic radiation, tar

mutation .... a random change in the base sequence or chromosome structure of a cell

NAD and NADP .... hydrogen carriers in respiration and photosynthesis respectively

natural selection .... the selection of individuals by nature to survive to breed – Darwin's theory

negative feedback .... a control mechanism to maintain the steady state

niche .... the position an organism occupies in an ecosystem, often with respect to its feeding

nicotine .... a plant defence compound, which can damage developing fetuses

nitrogen .... an essential element needed for the manufacture of protein

non-disjunction .... a form of mutation where chromosomes or chromatids fail to separate during meiosis

nucleic acids .... deoxyribonucleic acid (DNA) and ribonucleic acid (RNA)

nucleotide .... a DNA/RNA sub-unit composed of a base, a sugar and a phosphate group

operator .... in the J-M hypothesis, a DNA sequence which switches on the structural gene

organelle .... a tiny structure, e.g. mitochondrion, found in cells

osmoregulation .... a form of homeostasis to keep the strength of solutions constant

osmosis .... the diffusion of water through a membrane from a hypotonic to hypertonic solution

oxidation/reduction reactions . reactions involving the loss of hydrogen (oxidation) or addition of hydrogen (reduction)

pancreas .... an animal organ which produces hormones, in particular insulin and glucagon

peppered moth .... a type of moth which has adapted to city life by a change in colour

permeability .... the ability of a membrane or cell wall to allow materials to pass through

phagocytosis .... a process carried out by some specialised cells to engulf particles or cells

phenotype .... the appearance of an individual with respect to its genotype

phenylketonuria (PKU) .... a human genetic disorder resulting from a missing enzyme

phospholipid .... a major chemical component of cell membranes

phosphorous .... an essential element found in, for example, ATP, DNA, RuBP, GP

photolysis .... part of the first stage of photosynthesis in which water is split using light energy

photoperiodism .... the effects of day-length on behaviour of some plants and animals

phototropism .... a growth response in plants, towards or away from light

pituitary gland .... an endocrine gland of the brain which produces, for example, ADH, GH and TSH

plankton .... microscopic floating organisms – both plants and animals

plasma membrane .... the membrane which surrounds a cell, composed of phospholipid and protein

plasmid .... a ring of DNA found in bacterial cells and used for genetic engineering

plasmolysed .... the appearance of a plant cell which is in a strongly hypertonic medium

polyploidy .... having more than the diploid number of chromosome sets

population .... a group of animals or plants of one species only ‡

population dynamics .... changes to sizes of populations over a period of time

potassium .... an essential chemical element needed by plants and animals

protoplast .... a plant cell without a cell wall, used in somatic cell fusion

pyruvic acid .... a 3-carbon compound formed at the end of glycolysis

recombinant DNA technology .. another term for genetic engineering

recombination of
    linked genes .... in meiosis, the swapping of genes at chiasmata

recombinant gametes .... the gametes formed as a result of crossing-over taking place

© Leckie & Leckie

Higher Biology Vocabulary List

reduced co-enzyme .... a hydrogen-transporting subunit of an enzyme, for example NAD

regeneration .... the regrowth of parts of an animal (e.g. antlers) or plant (e.g. roots)

regulator gene .... in the J-M hypothesis, a gene which produces the repressor molecule

replication .... the duplication of DNA

repressor molecule .... in the J-M hypothesis, a molecule which stops the operator from working

resin .... a compound produced by some plants at wounds for protection

respiratory substrate .... an energy-rich substance, e.g. glucose, fat or protein, used for respiration

restriction enzymes .... a group of enzymes, e.g. endonuclease, used for cutting DNA

ribose/deoxyribose sugar ...... sugars found in nucleic acid molecules (RNA and DNA respectively)

ribosome .... a tiny structure where proteins are synthesised in cells

rickets .... a bone disorder in humans resulting from lack of vitamin D or calcium

mRNA .... a nucleic acid which carries the genetic code from the nucleus to the ribosomes

tRNA .... a nucleic acid which transfers specific amino acids to the ribosomes

rooting powder .... an artificial plant hormone used to stimulate the growth of roots

RuBP .... a 5-carbon chemical which fixes carbon dioxide during the Calvin cycle

salmon migration .... the movement of salmon from fresh water to the sea and vice-versa

selective breeding .... the selection of particular animals and plants by humans for breeding

selective ion uptake .... the uptake of particular ions by cells by active transport

sessile .... being fixed to one spot, as in plants

sex-linked genes .... genes which are found on the X (or occasionally Y) chromosome

shade plant .... a plant adapted to growing in the shade – one with a low compensation point

social hierarchy .... see dominance hierarchy

somatic fusion .... the fusion of ordinary plant cells (not gametes) in genetic engineering

specific .... of enzymes – acting only on one substrate;
of antibodies – acting only on one type of antigen

spindle fibres .... protein filaments which attach to chromosomes during mitosis or meiosis

spring/summer wood .... the xylem vessels of spring wood are larger in diameter than those of summer wood

stomata .... pores in leaves used for gas exchange. Each one is surrounded by two guard cells.

structural gene .... in the J-M hypothesis, a gene which codes for an enzyme

substitution .... a form of mutation in which one base is replaced by another

succession .... the change in the composition of plant communities over a long period of time

tannin .... a compound produced by some plants for protection

territorial behaviour .... the protection of an area for sole usage by one or more animals

tissue .... a group of similar cells working together to perform one function

transcription .... the transfer of the genetic code from DNA to mRNA

translation .... the interpretation of the genetic code in terms of the amino acid sequence

translocation .... a mutation in which a piece of chromosome is moved from one place to another

transmission of light .... the passage of light through leaves

transpiration .... the loss of water from a plant by evaporation

transpiration stream .... the pathway of water movement through plants from roots to leaves

triplet code .... a set of 3 of the bases: adenine, guanine, thymine and cytosine. It codes for 1 amino acid.

thyroid gland .... an endocrine gland in the neck which produces thyroxine

thyroid stimulating
    hormone (TSH) .... produced by the pituitary gland to stimulate the thyroid gland

turgid .... describing a plant cell full of water and firm as a consequence of this ‡

unicellular organisms .... one-celled organisms, e.g. amoeba, paramecium

vasoconstriction .... a decrease in the bore of a blood vessel to decrease heat loss from the body

vasodilation .... an increase in the bore of a blood vessel to increase heat loss from the body

virus .... the smallest 'living' thing, composed principally of nucleic acid and protein

vitamin D .... a vitamin needed for absorption of calcium and hence the growth of bones

wildlife reserves .... places to protect endangered species

xerophytes .... plants, e.g. cacti, adapted to survive in very dry conditions

xylem .... tissue which makes up wood and transports water and mineral salts in plants

© Leckie & Leckie